Ever Since Adam and Eve

A pictorial narrative of the Battle of the Sexes
in original drawings by famous cartoonists

Edited and with contributions by
ALFRED ANDRIOLA *and* MEL CASSON

McGRAW-HILL BOOK COMPANY, INC.
New York   Toronto   London

Library of Congress Catalog Card Number: 55–10401

Published by the McGraw-Hill Book Company, Inc.

Printed in the United States of America

We,
the editors,
with
premeditation
and in collusion,
dedicate
this book
TO THE
NATIONAL
CARTOONISTS
SOCIETY,
to
cartoonists
everywhere,
and to
their parents
who put up
with them
when they are
learning how
to draw
and laboring
over funny
things to say

Acknowledgments

The editors wish to express their deep appreciation to the cartoonists whose original work appears in this book for their cooperation in making the collection possible, and to the following syndicates and magazines which graciously permitted the use of copyrighted characters: *Chicago Sun-Times* Syndicate; *Chicago Tribune–New York News* Syndicate, Inc.; *Collier's*; Consolidated News Features, Inc.; Editors Syndicate; King Features Syndicate; NEA Service, Inc.; National Newspaper Syndicate; Post-Hall Syndicate, Inc.; Publishers' Syndicate; *Register* and *Tribune* Syndicate; and United Features Syndicate, Inc.

The editors further wish to express their appreciation to Ed Kuhn for his patience, understanding, and invaluable assistance in dealing with 86 assorted comic geniuses.

Contents

Hooked!

The Middle-age Spread

The Last Stand

Out of This World

Ever since...

MANY, MANY YEARS AGO, before man could write, he began to draw, and he recorded his fables and foibles on the walls of caves. This was before the day of agents, publishers, syndicates, gag men, art dealers, and salesmen; it was before he knew he could get money for his drawings. It was before money.

Nowadays, cartooning is a big business operated in a spare bedroom. A cartoonist has few weapons—a piece of paper, a bottle of ink, a pen, and an idea. Since he needs very little space in which to gestate and suffer through his labor pains, he is usually relegated to "that room" in the house or apartment which in a more normal ménage would contain the sewing machine, the mops and pails, trunks full of old letters and baby shoes. In conversation at the cocktail party, his wife always refers to this room as "the studio."

Here, in his cubicle and his isolation, the cartoonist records the humors, good and bad, of modern man, for magazines, books, and newspapers. Here he laughs at the world and himself, and hopes the world will laugh with him. If it does, he's in business.

Will Shakespeare wrote that man has seven ages, and each in his time plays many parts. We asked our fellow cartoonists to join us in illustrating the battle of the sexes through these ages and to go beyond Shakespeare by one. We have designated eight, tracing man's journey from maternity to eternity, picturing his triumphs, defeats, and stalemates in the longest war of all time—the one which began in the Garden of Eden.

When Adam saw what a thing of beauty God had fashioned of his bony rib, he gazed longingly at Eve—and the world began. We have it on reliable authority (an ancestor of ours was there) that his first words were "Hooray for the little difference!" After the much publicized Snake and Apple incident, our original ancestors first noticed they were without clothes. (Apparently neither of them was very observant.) Next they packed up their fig leaves and forsook the Garden for the cold, cruel world. At least, they reassured themselves, they had each other. For without Adam, Eve would have been only a spare rib. And without Eve, Adam would still be munching sour apples.

From that day to this, Man and Woman have lived together in various degrees of harmony and discord. For love of a woman, man has conquered nations singlehanded, wrestled with lions, scaled the highest peaks, swum the Hellespont, and washed the dishes. And Woman has baked apple pies, knitted socks, painted nails, plucked brows, and haunted local beauty parlors, solely for the love of a man. But whether it be Romeo and Juliet, David and Bathsheba, or Li'l Abner and Daisy Mae, they all have the same idea in mind— to work out some *modus vivendi* that stands at least a chance of lasting a lifetime.

A few of our cartoonists have found in the male-female relationship all the world's happiness. The majority, however, caught their boys and girls, wolves and vamps, mas and pas in conflict, because it is always more humorous, more biting, more tickling to deal with war—at least in this domestic field—than with peace. Libraries are stacked with books about the tempestuous affairs of Antony and Cleopatra, Samson and Delilah, Scarlett O'Hara and Rhett Butler. None went smoothly; each was entertainingly violent. But relatively little has been recorded about the peaceful affair of John and Sally Slockmeyer who live in that little white house off Main Street with their three children.

The truth is, there is nothing to report about a dormant volcano. But as soon as the crater erupts, it makes black headlines in every newspaper. It is the same with two people necking in a hammock and not really listening to Guy Lombardo's this-side-of-heaven music on the phonograph. Nobody cares. But should they bust out into a good old-fashioned donnybrook—should she smash a stack of unbreakable records over his head and precipitate his hasty exit— every wig in town starts wagging.

And so it is primarily the hot war that is recorded in this book— with humor, with acid, and, we hope, with affection.

Alfred Andriola
Mel Casson

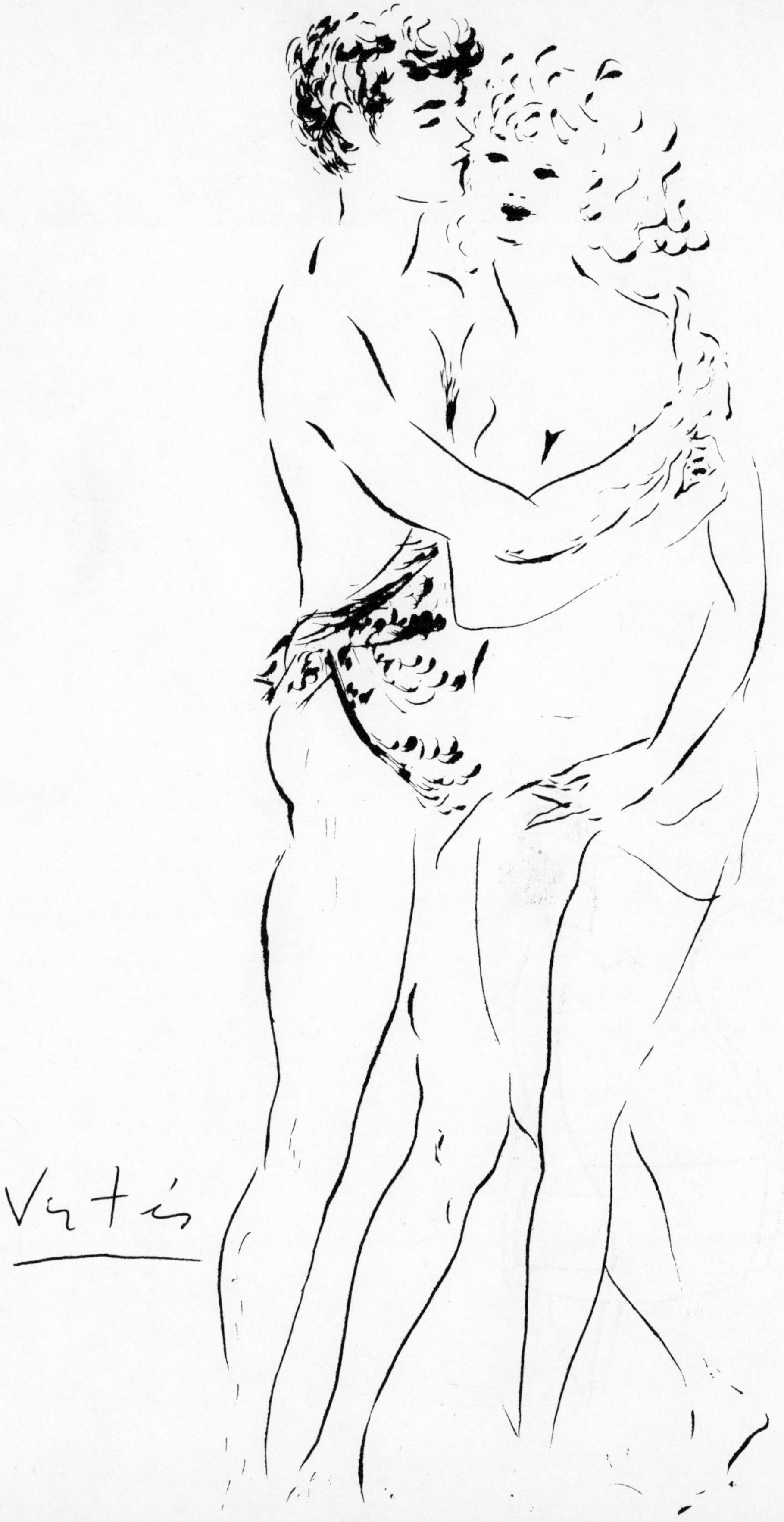
Vertès

Love in Bloom!

THE ORIGIN OF THE SPECIES, Mr. Darwin to the contrary, is the union of man and woman, but that shouldn't be a revelation to anybody. There has been no improvement in this field since the very beginning, and it is about the only thing the Russians have not laid claim to inventing.

The unborn child spends roughly nine months with a pregnant mother and a prostrate father. As the days pass, the mother looks more and more as though she has swallowed a globe of the world. Then one day she can no longer tie her own shoelaces, or squeeze behind the steering wheel. By this time the father has been reduced to a mass of jangled nerves and is thankful that, except for "the little difference," this might all be happening to him!

The incubating heir makes his initial appearance squalling and resisting. Yet this reluctant star of the drama invariably steals the stage. From the moment of his arrival, every gurgle, cough, sneeze, smile, word, cry, tooth, step, fall, bruise, intake and output is of momentous concern to his parents—and a paralyzing bore to their friends.

Here are a few of the whimsies, pains, and incongruities of this first stage of man's development leading up to his initial clash with another human being—a doctor's firm slap on his bare backside!

4   *Women should know about maternity. Dorothy*
   McKay's work appears in Esquire . . .

"I'm going to have mine the natural way . . .
                    breathing and all that."

"Honey! . . . Are we having a baby?"

Marcel Vertès, renowned for his sophisticated people, shows maternity on the Riviera . . .

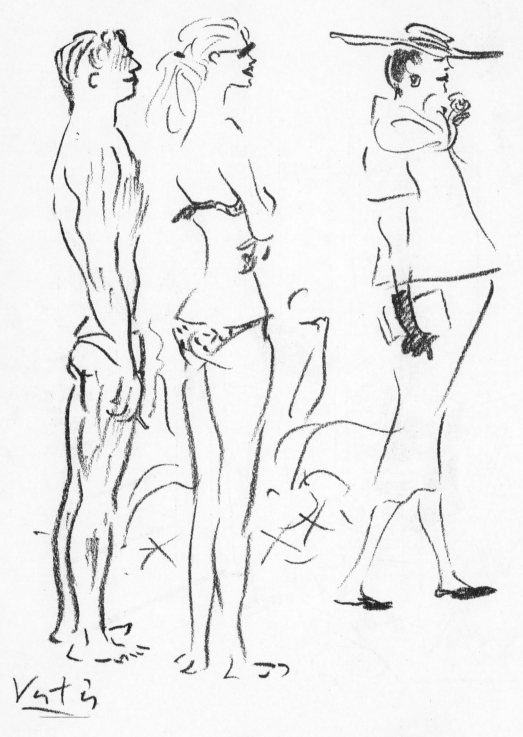

"She always tries to look different."

"Oh, I meant to tell you—it wasn't
psychosomatic after all."

In simple, direct lines, Chon Day pinpoints
real and amusing circumstances . . .

"Oh, oh!"

With deft strokes, Henry Syverson of The Saturday Evening Post *tells a story without words . . .*

"Good gracious! I just realized
I don't know a single lullaby!"

"If it's true about babies, the Smiths
are gonna have two of them!"

"Which of you is Mr. Bingham?"

The Small and the Mighty

THE SECOND STAGE of life is filled with pratfalls and pitfalls. Little Adam can now walk and talk. In his own diabolic and angelic way he is master of the house. He dominates his parents, bullies his dog, and wins every battle with his Teddy bear. He is perfectly happy in his imperialistic world, the czar of his little Utopia. *This is living!*

Then it happens. One day somebody walks in the door, no bigger than he is, and not much different, really. Her hair is longer, her eyes are bluer, and her jeans may be a little cleaner. Her name, she says, is Eve. She picks up his Teddy bear and pulls off an ear. Little Adam does what any self-respecting male must do. He hauls off and socks her in the jaw. Great juicy tears roll from Eve's blue eyes and down her cheeks. The stone of Adam's heart melts to butter. From this moment on, his Utopia is gone and he is lost. He will never again be able to "go it alone."

Though she may play with dolls and he with marbles, their relationship prospers in ignorance of the "little difference." Life is as yet uncomplicated by glands and nothing rears its head except Mama to announce that dinner is ready.

Hank Ketcham's incomparable "Dennis the Menace" rarely allows anyone to get the best of him.

"What do ya expect? I'm only five years old."

"Ah, *there* you are, Miss Philbrick! I believe the next dance is ours."

Irwin Caplan

18 *Charles Schulz's comic strip, "Peanuts," features
a younger generation wise before its time.*

'What do you mean, girls can't fly kites,
Charlie Brown? It's up, isn't it?"

SLUGGO
LOVES
NANCY
© 1955, United Features Synd., Inc.
SLUGGO
LOVES
NANCY
JUDY
ABBY
VERA
DOT
FLO
-ERNIE BUSHMILLER

Punch's *brilliant satirist, Ronald Searle, converts the child's world into a sardonic romp* . . .

"Why don't you let down your hair or something?"

Ulysses

The female logic is pointed up by Ed Nofziger,
creator of "Animal Antics" . . .

"That's a man for you—no sense of values."

"This is the reason I gave up playing with dolls."

"It's frightening, isn't it—
what we grow up to be!"

Harry and Wende Devlin produced six children and put them in their feature, "Full House."

Editors Synd. 1955

Harry DEVLIN

"Mother, is there anything besides boys we can marry?"

"One thing about dames—you can
get along without them!"

England's J. W. Taylor of Punch *magazine shows
a child's happy dream world . . .*

1955 The Register and Tribune Synd.

"But you won't be a gent for a couple of years yet!"

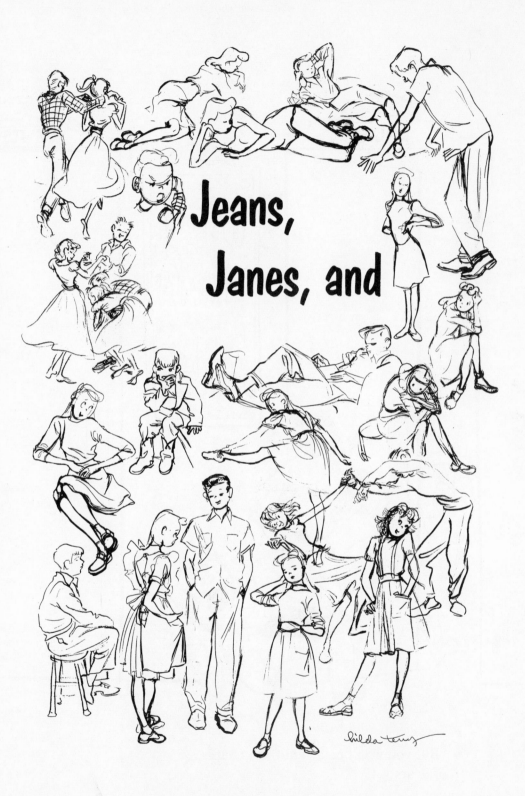

Jeans,
Janes, and

Growing Pains

ONE DAY the girl next door looks at the boy down the street. Suddenly, for the first time in her life, she knows what she wants and she is on the field of battle. Instinctively she arrays her colors and collects her weapons—a lipstick, a compact, and a sloppy sweater.

For a while the male may be the unsuspecting victim. His mind, poor innocent soul, is on other things—why an F-80 jet buffets as it breaks through the sound barrier, or what size shoe Willie Mays wears. But he knows nothing about girls. As time goes on, he'll know even less.

This doesn't disturb the girl next door. She likes it that way. Wars have been won before by the element of surprise. She analyzes her prey and sets a junior-size trap, baiting it with a drop or two of Midnight Sin under the left ear. He trips over his dirty saddle shoes and falls into it. Coming up for air, he finds his heart dangling on her charm bracelet, like a shrunken head on a cannibal's spear.

The janes—and the genes—are in motion. Forward, troops!

George Clark's "The Neighbors" warmly portrays
a cross section of America with truth and humor.

"He's ideal for Jane. He has all the qualities
she likes to change in a boy."

"I'm trying to warn you about men, Alicia—
stop screaming 'How wonderful!' "

Barbara Shermund knowingly pinpoints a girl's way with a man in "Shermund's Sallies."

"Well, there's one thing—she certainly isn't controversial!"

"I think I oughta drop Hughie. . . . I'm learning too
much about boys from him, and not enough about men."

*The well-populated drawings of Carl Rose, re-
nowned book illustrator and cartoonist . . .*

"Stop following me around!"

Fourteen

Fifteen

Sixteen

. . . *appear in* The New York Times Magazine, section, The Atlantic Monthly, *and* This Week.

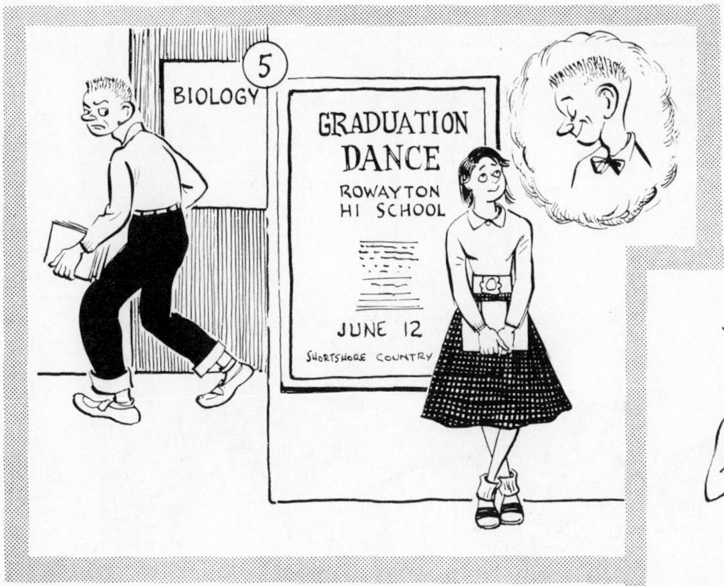

Seventeen

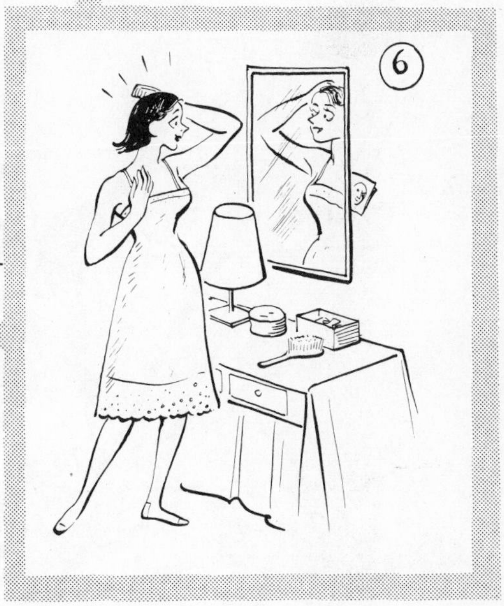

Eighteen

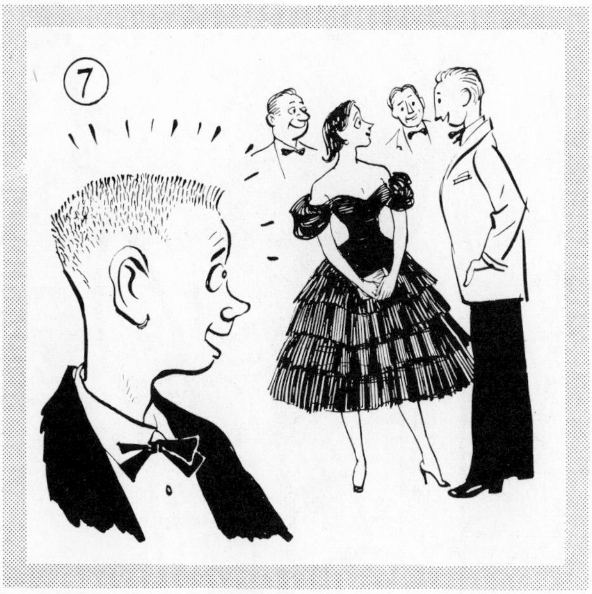

Nineteen

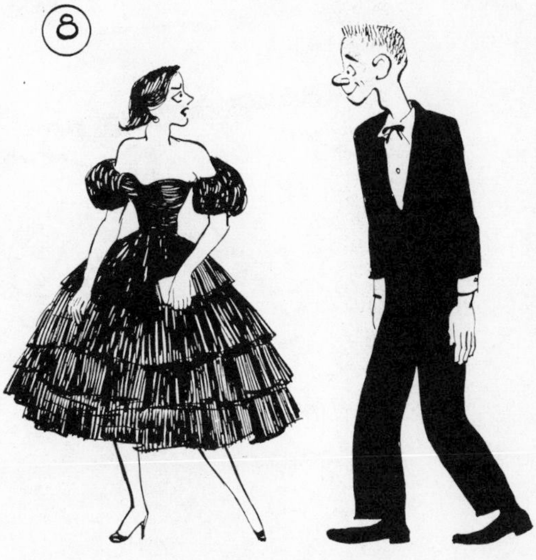

"Stop following me around!"

"How can you say such horrible things, Father?
Fred's the most popular boy in school!"

"Any volunteers to bisect a curve?"

Marty Links is one of the top teen-age delineators in "Bobby Sox" . . .

"No, this is *not* the home of Emmylou Meriweather—
this is Grand Central Station!"

"Oh, Ronny, you shouldn't have. My father just planted that bush."

"Nothing doing! If this is Dutch treat, I'm
handing my money to the waiter myself!"

Osborn

Hot on the Trail

This section is dedicated
to the men and women
who so tenaciously struggle
on this battlefield of lust and romance
and chase each other
into a state of holy matrimony.

Here men (and women too)
depict in words and pictures
how the battle of the sexes,
consisting of the pass and impasse,
is fought on this hallowed ground.

On the next pages, seven bright stars of
The New Yorker *magazine . . .*

"Abercrombie here suggests a merger."

"Time to go home? But she's still
upstairs getting dressed!"

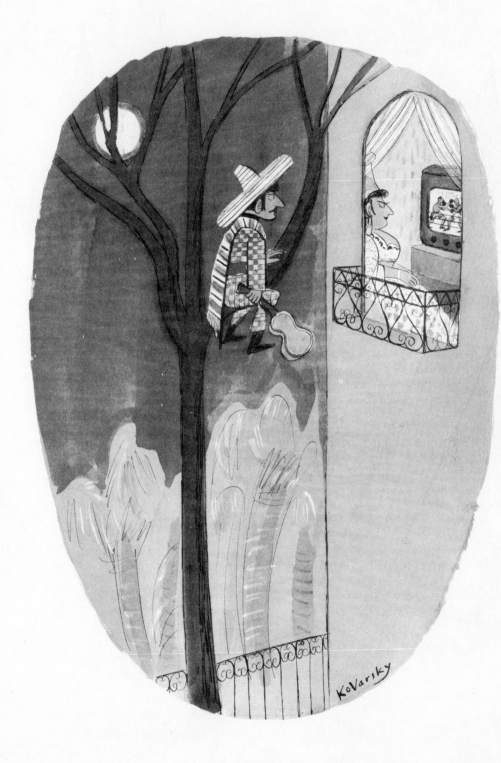

"I like that slogan you have. It's
the same as mine."

"Separate checks, please!"

"Where in the world are all the annoyers
tonight?"

"Would you call a cab for Mr. Jessup."

Without doubt one of the outstanding "pretty girl" artists of our time . . .

"But you said it was a Bal Masqué!"

Milton Caniff, superb adventure-strip artist, created a vogue as seen in "Steve Canyon."

*Here he satirizes his own style in which the hero,
even in villain's disguise, must triumph.*

© 1955, Field Enterprises, Inc.

Punch *magazine brings forth another great cartoonist, Ionicus—so very British.*

"So *this* is where your etchings are!"

"Your mural dresses up the barracks fine, *Killer*—
but where are the light switches?"

In a series of drawings, Campbell Grant,
illustrator of humorous books . . .

Samson and Delilah

Siegfried and Brünnhilde

Helen of Troy and Paris

Antony and Cleopatra

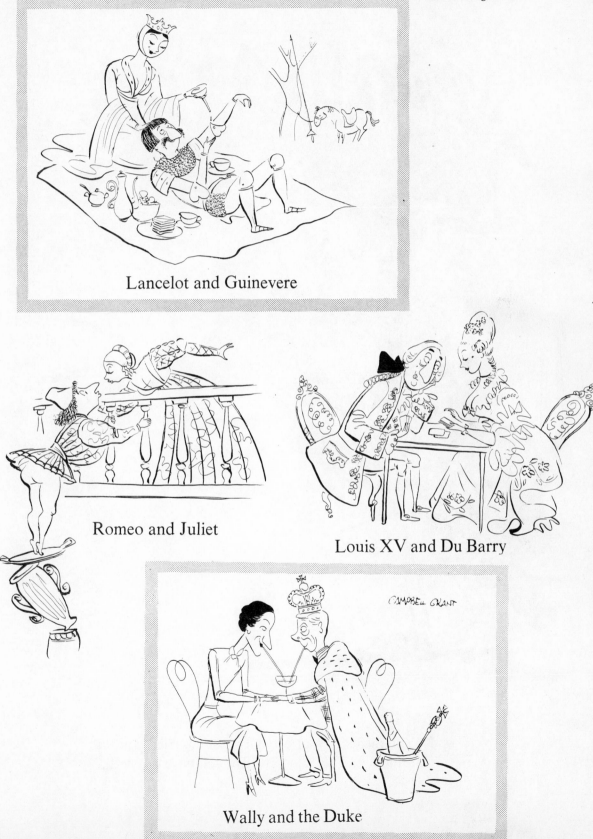

Lancelot and Guinevere

Romeo and Juliet

Louis XV and Du Barry

Wally and the Duke

"You mean all four of your wives married you for your money? That's terrible. Do you have any left?"

"He's a big-game fisherman. You should hear the tall stories he tells."

MARY 2 — PREFERS A COUNT TO AN ACCOUNTANT; MARRIES

PETER — HAS AN AFFAIR WITH

DIVORCED BY

MARY 5 (SEE 2)

MARRIES RACE TRACK GAMBLER

MARION — MARRIES — LOVES

HER BOSS — HAS OFFICE ROMANCE WITH

MICHAEL — LOST IN LOVE, ENTERS MONASTERY

BUGSY — RUNS OFF WITH BALLET DANCER

SHIRLEY — MARRIES

MIRA — DITCHES EVERYTHING FOR CAREER

HARRY — TAKES UP WITH NIGHT CLUB SINGER

MR. BUCKS

GOES INTO DEEP ANALYSIS; GOES TO DENMARK; BECOMES HARRIET

CAN-CAN — HAS AFFAIRS WITH

LOVES

..AND ROUND AND ROUND IT GOES!

JOHN (SEE 1)

WILBUR (SEE 3) — EMBEZZLES BANK FUNDS FOR ROMANCES; JUGGED

PHILIP — BECOMES MISSIONARY; DISCOVERS NATIVE GIRLS

Mel Casson goes to a Greenwich Village art show.

"You and your bright sales ideas. We haven't sold a painting in two days!"

High Fashion

Alex Raymond, creator of "Rip Kirby," shows a sample of his fine draftsmanship.

"I left when he wanted to show me how his outfit in Korea captured Hill No. 234 and Hill No. 235."

"Someday I'm going to write a book called
Blondes Prefer Gentlemen!"

Abner Dean is one of the classic interpreters of the battle between men and women. Whether you're a Dean-cultist or not, we consider this group of original drawings a collector's item. He made them earlier—before his wonderful books burst on the world.

False Security

Bravado

The Prize

Impasse

Fatalist

Trial Approach

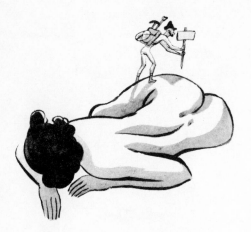

Delusion of Grandeur

One Minute to Curtain

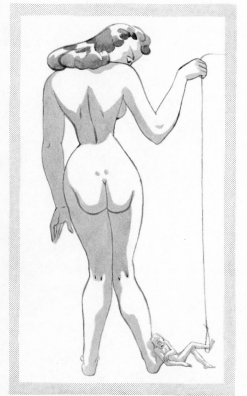

The Proposal

Surprise Ending

Exploratory Interlude

Futile Dialogue

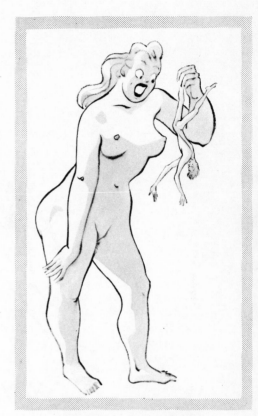

A Mind of Her Own

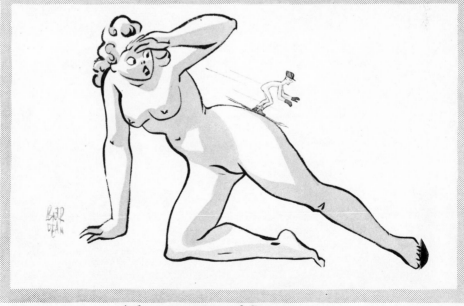

Adventure out of Season

Hooked!

"I NOW PRONOUNCE YOU man and wife!"

With this sentence (we mean it only in the grammatical and not the judicial sense), Man and Woman become one, sharing one roof, one bed, and one name. Married friends of ours (the authors of this book just happen to be bachelors, by intention and design) tell us that the purpose of life is fulfilled in love, companionship, a home, and children.

That is, some married friends tell us that. Others, who may be franker or more realistic, occasionally mention 2 A.M. feedings, beauty parlor bills, "other women." The more sensational short-comings of marriage dominate the tabloids and the gossip on the party line.

It would seem to be these negative aspects, these chinks in the armor of married life, that offer the vulnerable spots of attack to cartoonists. Judging from the drawings that follow, they wryly report the debit rather than the credit side of the picture.

Here you will find Man and Woman in crises that follow naturally after that all-important "I do." Now that they have succumbed to those syrupy Irving Berlin lyrics, they can try them out for themselves: the moon in June; the cozy cottage; "the boy for you and the girl for me."

But somehow the songs don't get around to mentioning the bills that start rolling in and the money that rolls out. The two kids become four—or six—and everybody stumbles over milk bottles and space helmets. Bit by bit he becomes used to seeing the girl of his dreams without her feminine defenses—sans makeup, sans girdle, sans everything. She, too, must watch her shining knight gradually become a paunchy, balding, sometimes unshaven creature of reality.

But with it all, through a series of what marriage counselors proudly call Adjustments, they have grown to love, honor, and cherish each other. And no one knows it better than the cartoonist who slashes at marriage with a cynical pen in his hand and an understanding wife at his side.

The problems of the young and married are pictured with unerring aim by Robert Day . . .

"I followed your mother's recipe just
the way she gave it to me."

"I told you, Betty—they're dead to the world."

"Certainly I'd like to go down in history—
but not like *that!*"

. . . *Martha Blanchard. Both appear in* The Saturday Evening Post, This Week, *and* Collier's.

79

"As it turned out, she never had any
intention of working after marriage."

"Now isn't it a fact that you won't listen
to logic unless I make a scene?"

Copr. 1955 by The Chicago Tribune

"You *would* be the one, Nina, to dream
that I was kissing a beautiful girl!"

82   *Another top husband-and-wife team, who operate individually as artists, are Greg d'Alessio and Hilda Terry. Here Greg (left) presents a cartoonist's-eye view of Hilda as wife and artist.*

"I told you I didn't have a thing to wear!"

"I just came across your old address book. Explain this 'deadbeat' next to my name!"

In two effective cartoons, Stan Hunt, of Collier's *and* The Saturday Evening Post . . .

"Here! Happy birthday, for God's sake!"

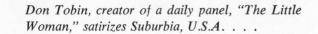

Don Tobin, creator of a daily panel, "The Little Woman," satirizes Suburbia, U.S.A. . . . .

"He and the steak have been marinating in wine for three hours."

"You're wasting your time, Don José Felipe.
I'm *not* going to give you a divorce!"

John Pierotti, sports cartoonist for the New York
Post, *goes as far as your next-door neighbor . . .*

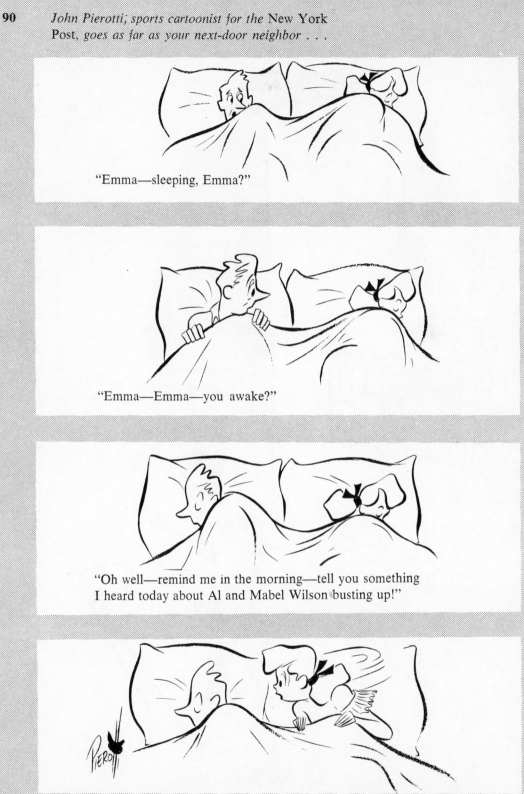

. . . and William de la Torre draws a world
of foreign people.

91

1.

2.

3.

4.

5.

de la Torre

The Middle-age Spread

THERE'S ONE NICE THING about middle age. You're not old. By this time, life has begun to fit like an old shoe—comfortable, if a bit run down. A woman knows she's going to do the laundry on Monday, play bridge on Tuesday, and go into town for a matinee on Wednesday. A man can look forward to bowling on Thursday, getting paid on Friday, and mowing the lawn on Saturday. The Sabbath being a day of rest, they rest.

Life, they have come to realize, is not a movie scenario. It is made up of honest little adventures rather than big dramatic ones. The kids have long since flown the nest and Mother and Father find themselves more or less where they started.

Pretty soon, like fine racing cars, their motors begin to slow down, there's more exhaust, it's harder going uphill, and they're in for repairs more often. Yet, no matter what physical changes occur —the color of the hair, the size of the waistline, the bags under the eyes, that fine print that keeps getting smaller and smaller all the time —one thing should never change: the magnetic appeal of the opposite sex. It may be harmless window-shopping, but a middle-aged man's head still turns around to admire a pair of trim ankles retreating on clicking heels, and a woman's ego never fails to soar when a male (not her husband, of course) gives her a passing look.

And this is the way it should be. It indicates the presence of what the French call *joie de vivre,* and the French know how to say it. We would simply call it "life"—and where there's life there's hope.

The cartoonists in this section examine the men and women, who, still huffing and puffing on the battlefield of love, have fallen heir to the middle-age spread.

*Syd Hoff's bold style brings his tenement
tenants wonderfully to life.*

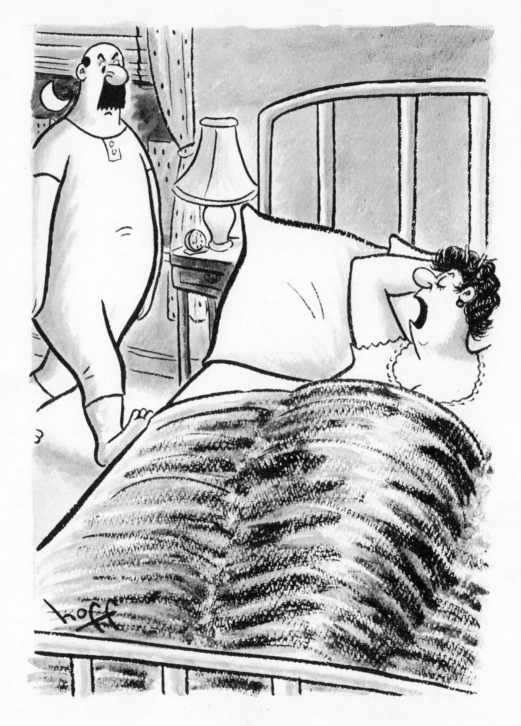

"All right, so I don't quiver when you
approach the bed. So what?"

"We don't have winters like that any more! I can remember having to dig out to the old pump through four feet of snow—thaw out the pump so we could water the stock!"

Our electric blanket didn't work last night! George nearly had a fit!"

F. B. Modell, who, like Claude Smith, appears in
The New Yorker, *adds a dash of pathos.*

"Goodness! What are you doing here already?
Homemakers' Jamboree is still on."

Claude Smith is one of the leading exponents of presenting a situation in a series of pictures.

*Otto Soglow, famous creator of "The Little King,"
uses one of the simplest styles in all cartoondom.*

O. SOGLOW

"Wife tells me you had bronchitis."

A bright star in the pantomime school is "Louie,"
a daily comic strip by Harry Hanan.

"Anything new at the office today, dear?"

Chaval, a brilliant French satirist, gets to the
point with sharp simplicity.

"George! You've been drinking!"

"Sometimes I don't think it's art he's
interested in at all."

"Harvey, remind me to pick up a quart
of milk on the way home."

From Punch, *two fine artists,*
David Langdon . . .

"I preferred it when he used to
blow his top about the bills."

Anton, one of England's best woman cartoonists, goes macabre.

"Isn't it time for your afternoon dip, Edna?"

"I love you. I love you. Can't you see
I've always loved you?"

Jay Irving, famous for his Collier's *cops, does a comic strip called "Pottsy."*

"Henry! You're not listening to . . . Henry!
You painted eyes on your eyelids!"

"And how is my little queen today?"

"Now here we go—all at once—and the pretty princess will be all better."

"Nasty old pain back again? Well now, let's see what we can do."

"So you've got a lousy backache . . . take an aspirin!"

The Last Stand

A CENTENARIAN who had spent most of his life with wine, women, and an occasional song was asked the secret of his longevity. After a moment's deep thought, he summed it up by saying, "Just keep breathing!"

That's one of the requisites. But there's more to old age than that. These are the days of looking back and remembering, for dreaming about youth and philosophizing about life. These are the nights when you're content to go to bed with a hot-water bottle and a warm memory.

Some ancient sage who must have spent a lifetime studying men, women, and strife once said, "The good Lord in His infinite wisdom created woman and made her beautiful so man could love her. Then He made her just a little bit dumb, so she could love man." And we might add, He made them both a little dependent on each other, so that they would need each other more and more as time went on.

The general picture of old age is a charming, white-haired couple sitting in a park feeding pigeons, or in rocking chairs on their own back porch sniffing the flowering hydrangea. But these are models for Currier and Ives prints; humor finds a treasure lode in those oldsters who may have snow on the roof but still have fire in the furnace. Before being put out to pasture, they take an occasional fling, often imaginary, at sowing a wild oat here and there. The cartoonists in this section deal primarily with these lusty souls for whom there is only one fitting epitaph: "There's life in the old boy yet!"

"... *Now* do you remember what day this is?"

". . . You wouldn't care to revise that part about attributing your re-markably long life and excellent health to breaking *all* the rules?"

"That's the sort of thing that lowers
the tone of the Crescent, Alice."

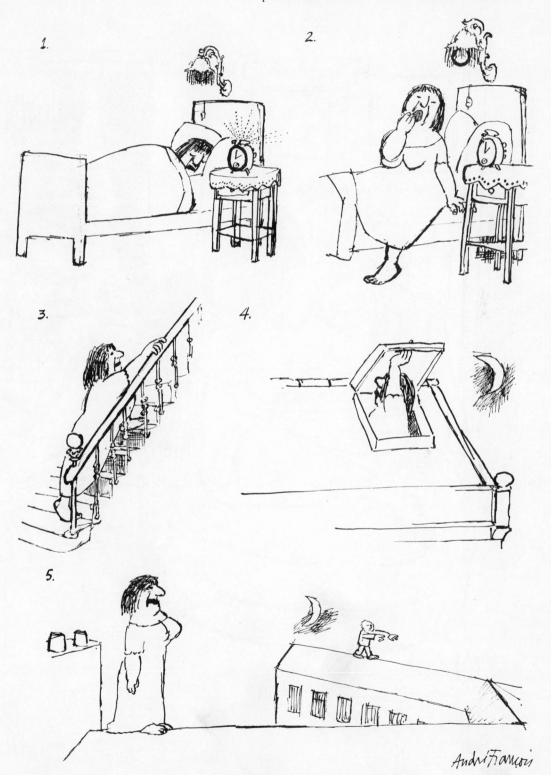

Mischa Richter's bold, slashing approach is well known in his daily panel "Strictly Richter" . . .

"Another rejection slip from *True Story* magazine!"

"Fifty years ago t'day, John! You were goin' to build a ruby
staircase to the stars for me to climb in pink satin slippers!"

"Three parts gin . . . one part vermouth . . . and a dash of aphrodisiac."

Frank Willard, master of the roughhouse humor in his comic strip "Moon Mullins" . . .

"Careful, Arthur. Remember your blood pressure."

Reamer Keller, who does a comic called "Kennesaw," and . . .

"Let me tell it! Some bold woman rushed up and kissed you and vanished before you could call a policeman!"

"Promise you'll think of me each time
you hock it, Miss Fenton."

"What's the matter—lost your nerve?"

"The Blodgets—how nice. You did get
George to come after all."

Out of This World

SHAKESPEARE traced man's progress from "the infant, mewling and puking" to the last scene of all, "second childishness and mere oblivion." But what happens in that oblivion is pictured differently in each man's mind, and we thought it would be fertile ground for this final phase of the battle of the sexes.

A group of imaginative satirists was asked to probe the unknown realm of angels and devils, to dissect with the sharp line and laughter of their pens the relationship of men and women after life. Does Man get the upper hand? Does Woman? Or is it still a draw? Is there retribution in the afterlife? Who strikes the last blow?

Since nothing on earth inhibits a cartoonist—except dull pencils and duller censors—we were sure nothing in heaven or hell would, either. On the following pages the cartoonists have entered a world not only of heaven and hell but of fantasy inhabited by satyrs, spooks, and spirits. Some of them have found the earthly status quo projected—angels and devils acting suspiciously like human beings. Others have mixed earthly and supernatural characters in improbable but discerning situations.

But all of them seem to conclude that out there where space and time form an endless infinity, man is still the man he has always been, and women are damn glad of it!

Noel Sickles, of Life *and* The Saturday Evening Post, *is one of our outstanding illustrators.*

"A boat trip always make me feel so alive!"

"Of course I love you, Gladys—I'm just
not ready to settle down yet."

"Dear—she just flew into the rectory!"

"Hmm! A lady people."

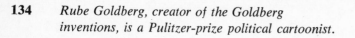
134 *Rube Goldberg, creator of the Goldberg inventions, is a Pulitzer-prize political cartoonist.*

"You idiot, can't you see they're all alike?"

"Mr. Stewart is resting comfortably . . .
Oh, just a minute, Mrs. Stewart."

136 *One of the best, Gregory d'Alessio does a daily panel, "These Women."*

"Colonel, there's a lady here who says she has proof positive that the Martians have made landings."

"Same old lousy housekeeper! Where's
my other wing?"

An encore for Virgil Partch, who appears in
Look *and* Collier's . . .

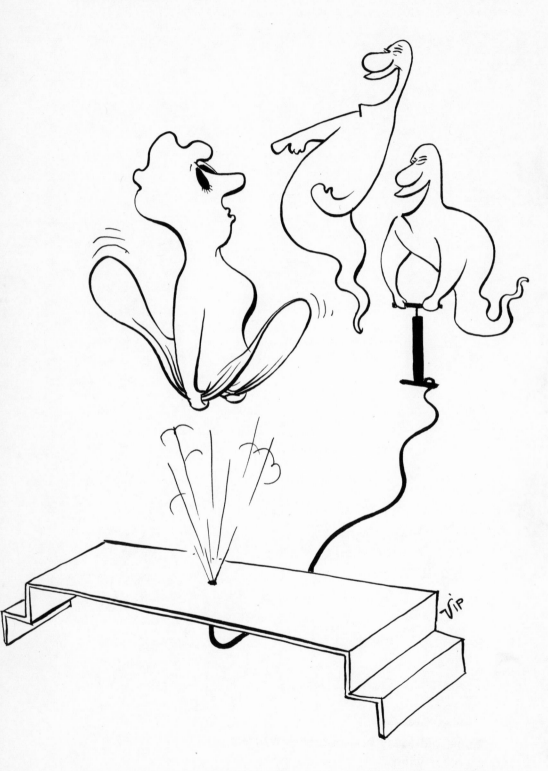

Al Capp is one of the few cartoonists who is as famous as his creation, "Li'l Abner."

"Enjoy yourself while you can, Bertram—
I won't live forever!"

"You were right, Martha; they were *not* mushrooms."

One of Japan's best, Taizo Yokoyama, deals perceptively with life after death.

REINCARNATION "You haven't changed a bit, dear."

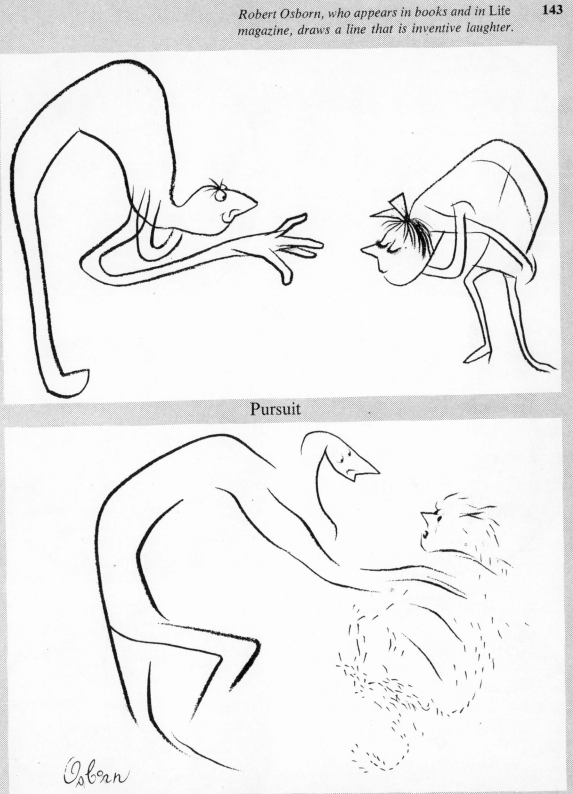

Pursuit

Removal of the Jupe

"I love you too, Roger, but how will I
explain to my family?"

ABOUT THE EDITORS

Alfred Andriola and Mel Casson are both New York bachelors and successful comic-strip artists. Here the similarity ends. Andriola was born in Greenwich Village, raised in Rutherford, New Jersey, and studied art at Cooper Union and writing at Columbia. Ultimately he decided against starving in a garret and combined his writing and drawing interests in an adventure strip. After a short apprenticeship in the profession, he made his initial appearance in the field with "Charlie Chan," an adaptation of the book and movie character. Eventually he started an original detective-adventure strip of his own, the extremely popular "Kerry Drake," which is now eleven years old and syndicated all over the country.

Mel Casson was born in Boston. Encouraged by his father, an able Sunday painter, to seek a career in art, Casson sold his first cartoon to The Saturday Evening Post *at the age of seventeen and afterward began to appear regularly in the* Post, Collier's, *the* Ladies' Home Journal, This Week, *and elsewhere. After an illustrious war record (he worked his way from infantry private to captain, participated in all major campaigns in Europe, was awarded two Bronze Stars and two Purple Hearts), Casson started his "Angel," a daily panel about the antics of a little girl. Today Angel's escapades are widely syndicated and appreciated throughout the country.*